Festivals

Paul Johnson

A & C Black · London

Reprinted 2003, 2005, 2007
First published 2001 by A & C Black Publishers Ltd
38 Soho Square, London W1D 3HB
www.acblack.com

ISBN 978-0-7136-5925-2

Copyright project ideas © Paul Johnson, 2001
Copyright illustrations © Kirsty Wilson, 2001
Copyright cover illustration © Alex Ayliffe, 2001

A CIP catalogue record for this book is available from the British
Library.

Printed in Great Britain by Caligraving Ltd, Thetford, Norfolk.

A&C Black uses paper produced with elemental chlorine-free
pulp, harvested from managed sustainable forests.

Contents

Introduction

How to use this book

Copy and Cut: Festivals provides a variety of photocopiable craft templates, each with simple instructions for children to follow. The templates enable children to make books, models and cards to celebrate festivals in the six major religions: Christianity, Judaism, Hinduism, Sikhism, Islam and Buddhism. The projects are ideal for use with the RE curriculum. They also provide innovative contexts for practising writing and literacy skills. There are opportunities for the children to read instructions and write text for a purpose, including stories, greetings and poems.

The projects are designed for six to eight year-olds, but many are also suitable for younger children. Any project can be easily adapted to your needs by masking and/or substituting text. Favourite templates can be removed from the book and filed with other relevant resources. At the back of the book, you will find photocopiable story texts for children to read and use for their own storybooks. There are notes for teachers which include practical suggestions and additional information on the featured festivals.

Preparation

First pull out the template page and cut around the border. Use this master page for all future photocopying (for an exact copy, lay the page on the photocopier plate rather than feeding it in.) To begin a project, photocopy both sides of the template for each child and check that the necessary resources are available (see 'You will need' for individual projects). Introduce the religion and the festival, and discuss ideas for the project. You may wish to read with the whole class one of the stories on pages 55–57. If necessary, demonstrate the making process. It is particularly useful to show the children how to hold the page to start with.

Some festivals have several projects linked to them; in this case you could plan for groups of children to work on different projects.

Decorating the projects

The templates can be reproduced on white or coloured paper or card, either as A4 or enlarged to A3. A3 is a particularly useful size for demonstration purposes and

storybooks. The instructions suggest basic decorating materials such as coloured pencils, to avoid requests for materials that may not be available. However, it would be useful to start a collection of extra resources, so that children can be more adventurous with their decorations to capture the vibrant nature of festivals. Suitable materials include glitter glue, pearlised paints, metallic pens and paper, coloured foil paper (especially gold, silver and red), sequin mesh, tinsel, holographic paper, art straws, sweet papers, wrapping paper, magazines, fabric and wool.

Tips for good results

Encourage the children to try out decoration ideas on an odd piece of paper first, and to plan in pencil. It's a good idea to avoid the use of fibre-tipped pens, as colours may run through the paper.

You could consider making two copies of the template for each pupil. One can be used for the rough draft and the other for the finished piece. If you copy the template on to card, show the children how to score along the dots with a pencil and ruler before folding. Children could word-process texts and stick them on to their finished card or book.

Ideas for display

These projects are perfect for school displays. Why not mount projects together on a classroom wall or in the school hall? Change the display throughout the year to celebrate the range of religious festivals.

Advent window

Advent is the four weeks leading up to Christmas Day. At this time, Christians look forward to celebrating Jesus' birthday on 25 December. An Advent calendar helps you count down the days to Christmas. Each day, open a window and see what's inside.

You will need: the Advent window template • scissors • pencil • pencil crayons, paint, glitter and glue for decorating

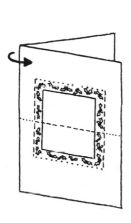

1. Fold the paper in half widthways, like this. Then unfold.

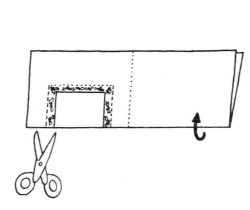

2. Fold the paper in half lengthways, like this. Cut along all the dashes.

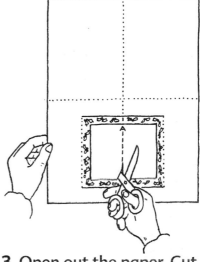

3. Open out the paper. Cut along the A dashes. Then fold the doors outwards along the dots.

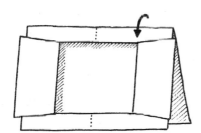

4. Now fold the paper in half widthways again.

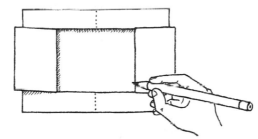

5. Inside your Advent window, draw a frame.

Open out the paper. Decide what you want to put inside the frame. You could draw a Christmas decoration, or write a Christmas joke or poem. Decorate the outside of the window with Christmas pictures and glitter. Don't forget to write a date on the doors.

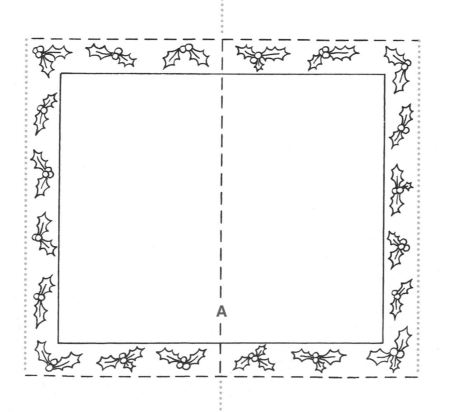

A

Nativity scene

Christmas is the time when Christians remember and celebrate Jesus' birthday. The Bible tells the story of how Jesus was born in a stable in Bethlehem, in Israel. This is called the Nativity story. You can show part of the story on your pop-up scene.

You will need: the Nativity scene template • the Nativity story • scissors • pencil • pencil crayons, coloured paper, fabric, cotton wool, glitter, straw or sand and glue for decorating

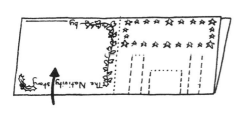

1. Fold the paper in half lengthways, like this.

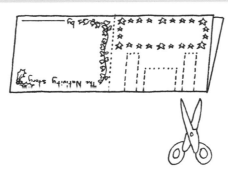

2. Cut along all the dashes.

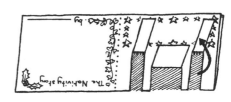

3. Fold the three strips forwards along the dots. Then fold them backwards. Unfold.

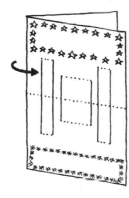

4. Open out the paper. Fold in half widthways, like this.

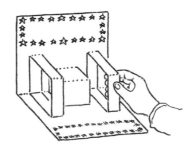

5. Fold the paper in half again. Now pull the pop-up shapes forwards.

Press your scene flat again. Read the Nativity story and decide what you want to show. You could draw Mary, Joseph and the baby Jesus on the pop-ups. Or you could show the shepherds on the hillside with their sheep. Write about the scene in the boxes. Remember to draw a picture on the front cover.

The kind innkeeper let them stay in his stable.

That night, Jesus was born.

The Nativity story

by _____

Christmas star

A bright, twinkling star shone over the stable where Jesus was born.
It showed that he was a special baby. Shepherds and wise men
followed the star to find Jesus. This is why stars
are important at Christmas time.

You will need: the Christmas star template • scissors • pencil • gold or silver pencils for decorating

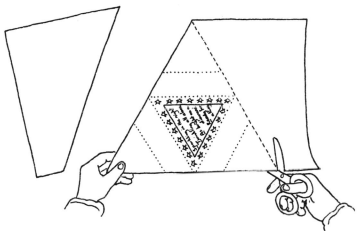
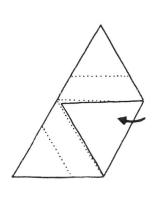

1. Cut along the dashes to make a triangle. Write a message in the middle.

2. Fold the paper forwards along all the A dots. Then unfold.

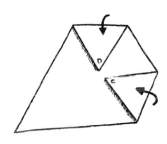
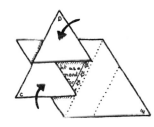
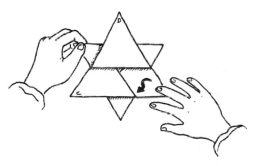

3. Turn the paper over. Fold backwards along all the B dots. Unfold. Then turn the paper over again.

4. Refold along all the dots to make your star. Start with C.

5. Carefully tuck the corner of E under the corner of C.

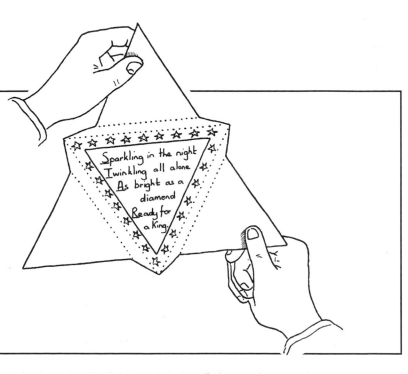

Your message could be a poem or words from a carol about the star that shone over baby Jesus. Colour the edges of the star gold or silver to make it shine. Put your star on top of a Christmas tree, or write a greeting on the back and give it to a friend.

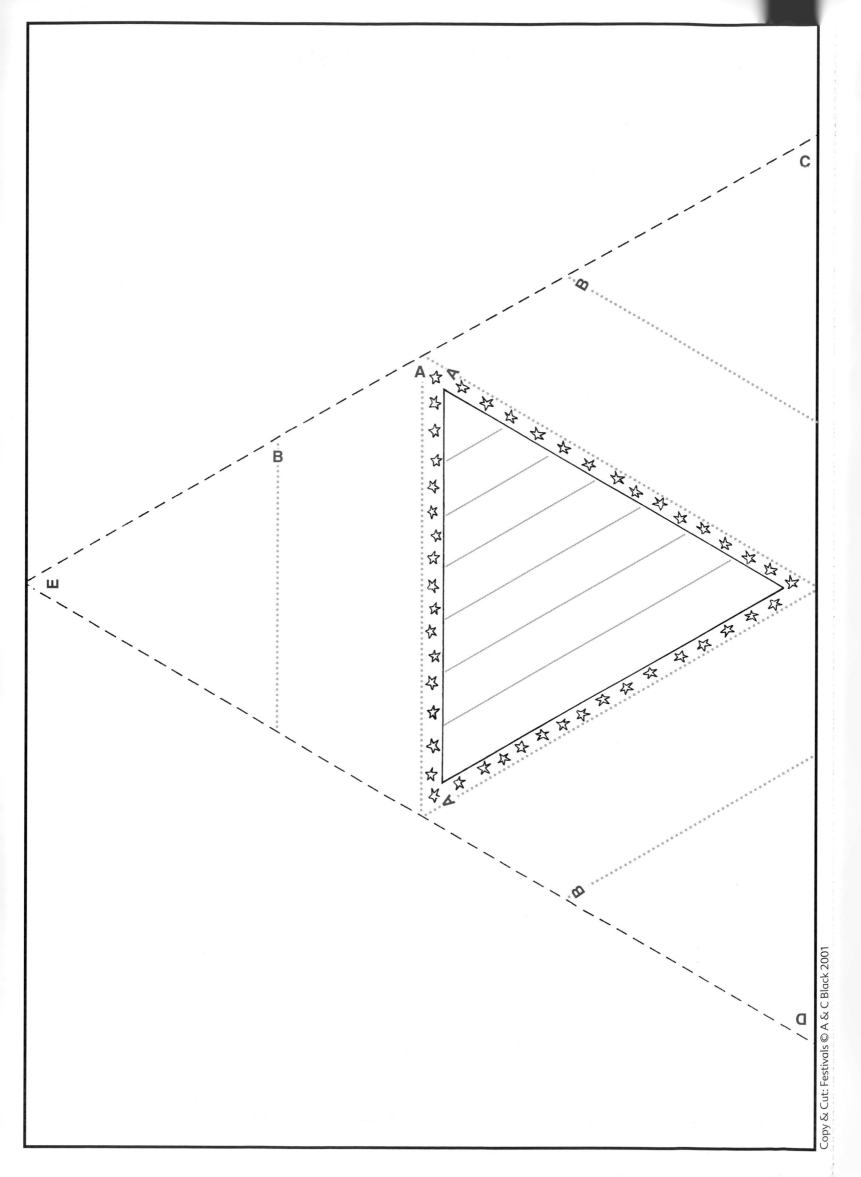

A

C

B

B

E

A

A

B

D

Angel card

On Christmas night shepherds were watching their sheep, when the sky was filled with brilliant light. Angels appeared and told the shepherds to go to Bethlehem and worship Jesus. 'Peace on Earth, goodwill to all people,' sang the angels.

You will need: the Angel card template • scissors • pencil • pencil crayons, tinsel, glitter and glue for decorating

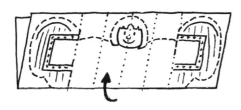
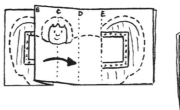
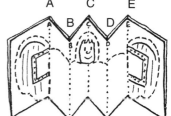

1. Fold the paper in half lengthways, like this.

2. Fold the paper in a zig-zag along the dots (A, B, C, D, E). Start by folding forwards along the A dots.

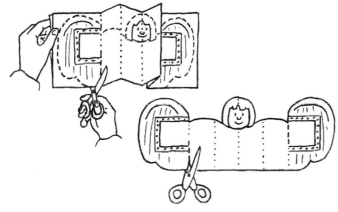
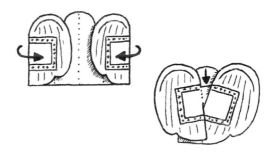

3. Pull open the zig-zag. Cut around the angel outline. Then cut along the dashes to make slots.

4. Decorate your angel. Then turn it over. Fold the wings forwards. Overlap the wings and slide the slots into each other.

Find pictures of angels to help you decide how to colour your angel. You could glue on a shiny halo made from tinsel and glue glitter on the angel's wings. Write a message on the back.

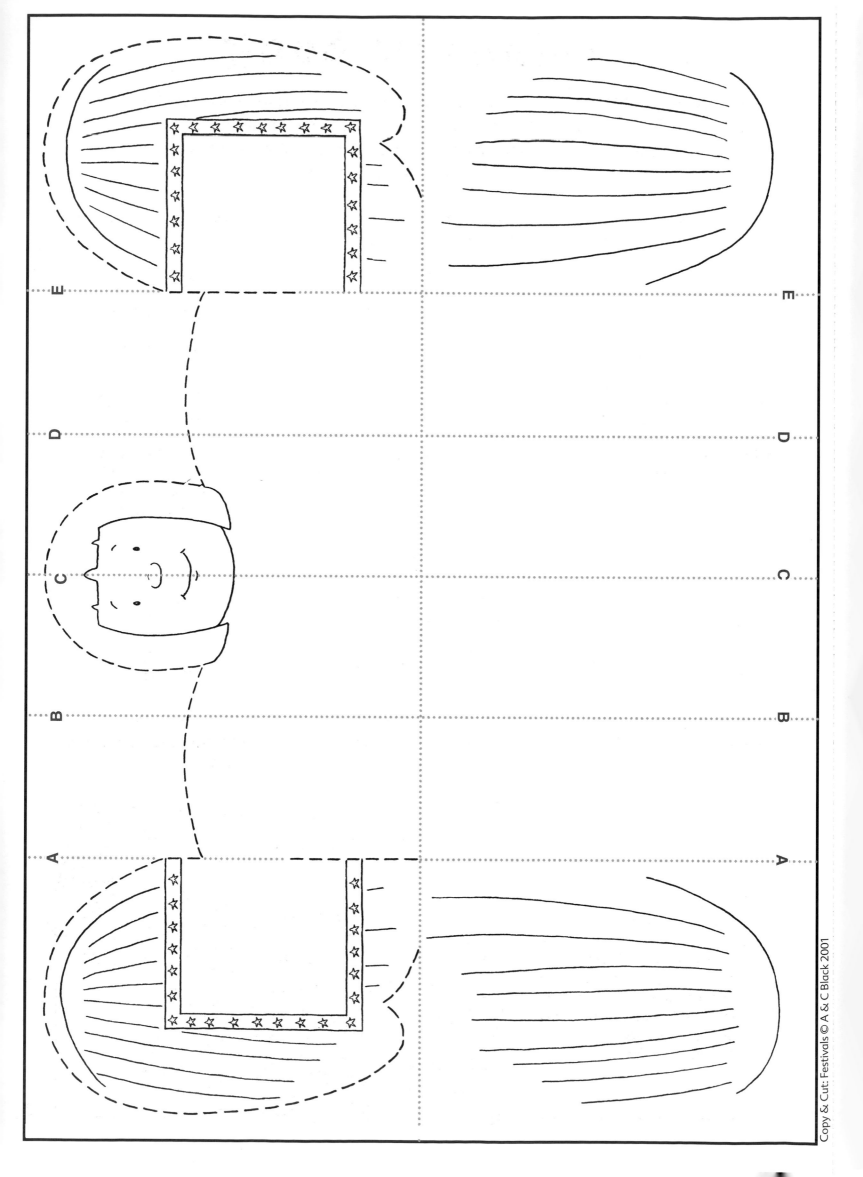

Epiphany book

Epiphany is the last day of Christmas, when it's time to take down the decorations. On this day, Christians remember the three wise men who visited the baby Jesus to worship him. The wise men brought precious gifts. Use this book to tell the story.

You will need: the Epiphany book template • the story of the three wise men • scissors • pencil • pencil crayons for decorating

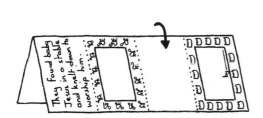

1. Fold the paper in half lengthways, like this.

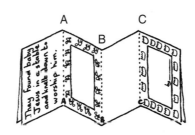

2. Fold the paper in a zig-zag along the dots (A, B, C). Start by folding forwards along the A dots.

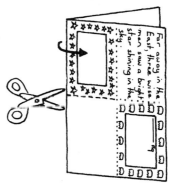

3. Open out the paper fully. Then fold in half widthways, like this. Cut along the dashes.

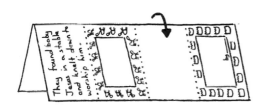

4. Open out the paper. Fold in half lengthways again.

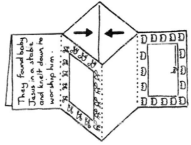

5. Push the left and right edges towards each other, so that you make a box shape in the middle. Keep pushing until the sides touch.

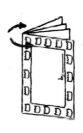

6. Find the blank page. Fold it around all the other pages.

Read the story of the three wise men. On the front cover of your book, write a title and your name. Inside, draw pictures to go with the story. Number the pages. To finish, write on the back cover what the book is about. Start with 'This book is about'.

Far away in the East, three wise men saw a bright star shining in the sky.

by
_____

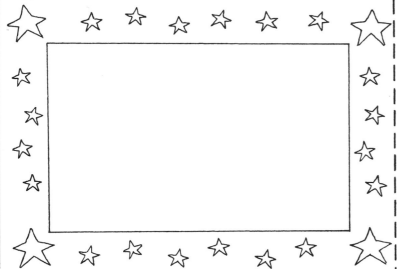

They followed the star to Bethlehem. They brought gifts of gold, frankincense and myrrh.

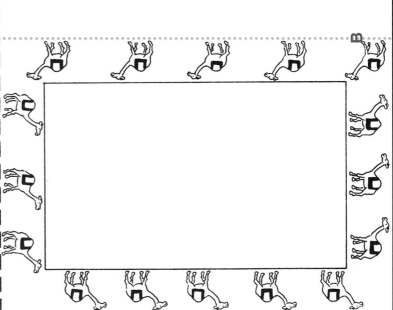

They found baby Jesus in a stable and knelt down to worship him.

Easter storybook

At Easter, Christians remember how Jesus died on a cross on Good Friday. But Easter is also a time to celebrate because Jesus came back to life on Easter Sunday. Tell the story of Easter in your own book.

You will need: the Easter storybook template • the Easter story • scissors • pencil • pencil crayons for decorating

1. Fold the paper in half lengthways, like this.

2. Fold the paper in a zig-zag along the dots (A, B, C). Start by folding forwards along the A dots.

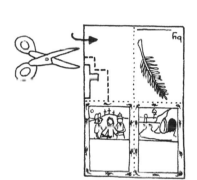

3. Open out the paper fully. Fold in half widthways, like this. Cut along the dashes.

4. Open out the paper. Fold in half lengthways again. Lift up the cross.

5. Fold the left and right edges forwards to make a book.

Read the Easter story. Look at the pictures in your book. Use the story to help you decide what to write beneath each picture. Don't forget to write your name on the front of your book.

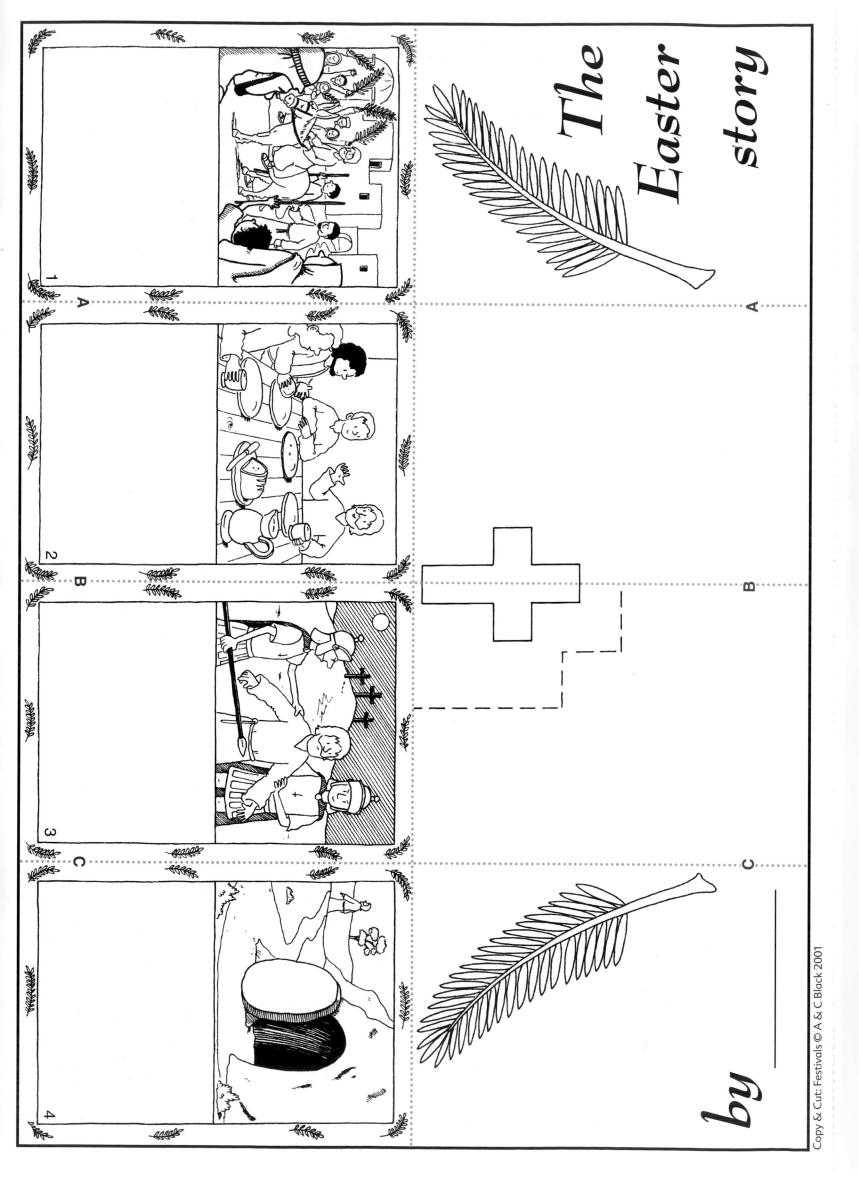

The Easter story

by _____

Easter chick

Easter is a time for celebrating new life. People give Easter eggs
and cards to each other. The eggs remind us it is springtime,
when many animals have their babies. Easter cards
often have pictures of eggs and chicks.

You will need: the Easter chick template • scissors • pencil • pencil crayons, coloured
paper and glue for decorating

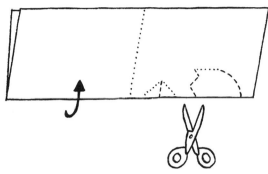

1. Fold the paper in half lengthways, like this.
Cut along all the dashes.

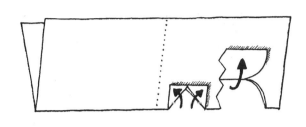

2. Fold the shapes forwards along the dots.
Then fold them backwards. Unfold.

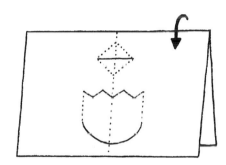

3. Open out the paper. Turn it round. Fold the
paper in half widthways, like this.

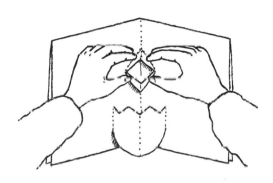

4. Fold the paper forwards to make a card. Pull
forwards the pop-up mouth and egg.

Write an Easter greeting inside
your card. Draw a chick hatch-
ing from the egg, or choose
another animal, such as a
dinosaur! Colour the egg
with bright patterns. For
the front of your card, cut
out a large egg shape from
coloured paper. Glue it on and
decorate it.

Have a
Quacking
Easter
Grandad

Love
Meg
X

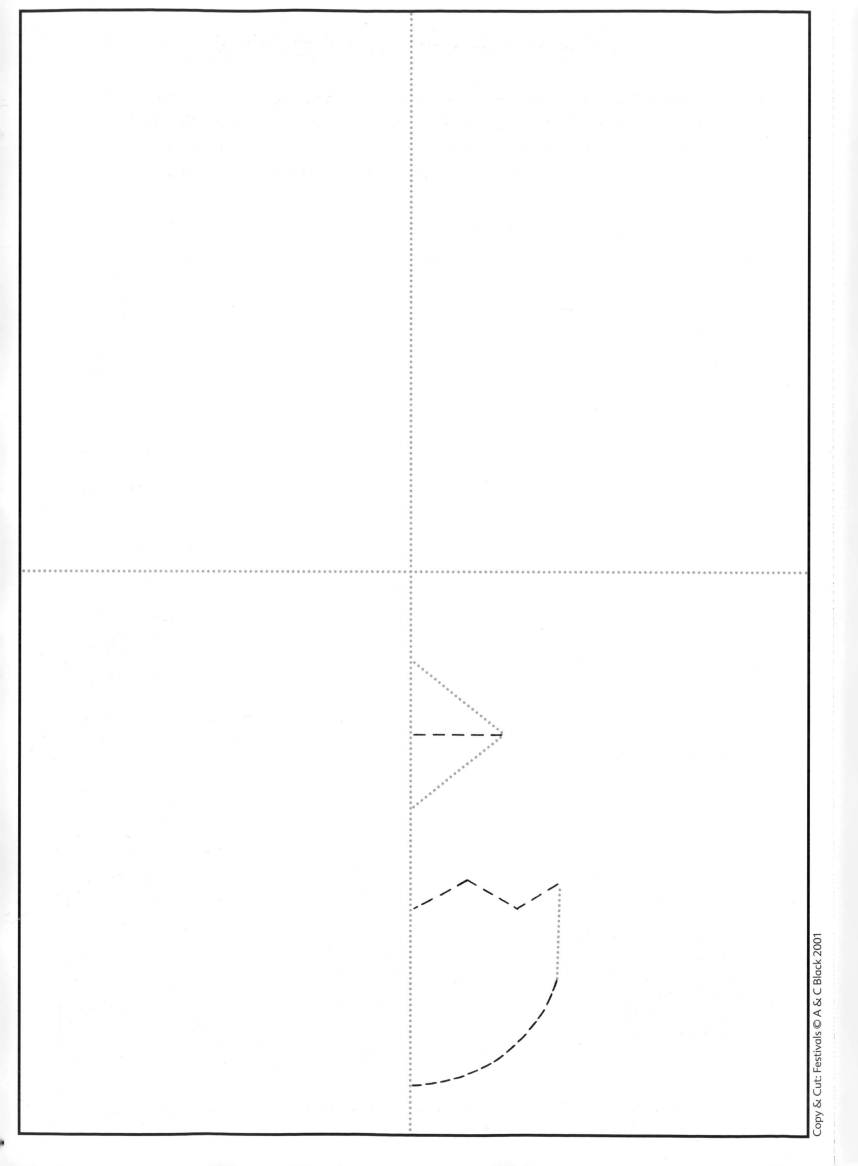

Harvest display

At harvest festival, Christians decorate churches with flowers, fruits and vegetables. This is to celebrate bringing in the harvest from the fields. People sing hymns to thank God for giving them food. Afterwards, the food in the church is given away to more needy people.

You will need: the Harvest display template • scissors • pencil • pencil crayons for decorating

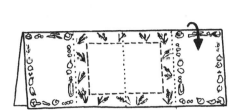

1. Fold the paper in half lengthways, like this.

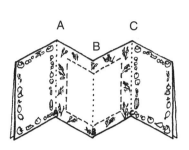

2. Fold the paper in a zig-zag along the dots (A, B, C). Start by folding forwards along the A dots.

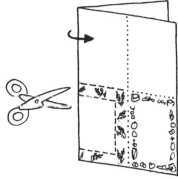

3. Open out the paper fully. Fold in half widthways, like this. Cut along all the dashes.

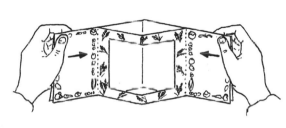

4. Open out the paper. Fold in half lengthways again. Push the left and right edges towards each other to make the display stand up.

5. Press the paper flat again. Inside the window, draw a frame.

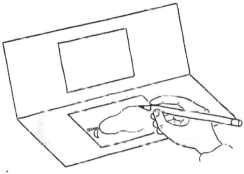

6. Open out the paper. Inside the frame, carefully draw a fruit or vegetable.

Fold the window back down. Then write about harvest-time next to the picture. You could find out more about the fruit or vegetable you have drawn. Write about where it comes from. Or make up a poem. Describe how the fruit or vegetable looks, smells and tastes.

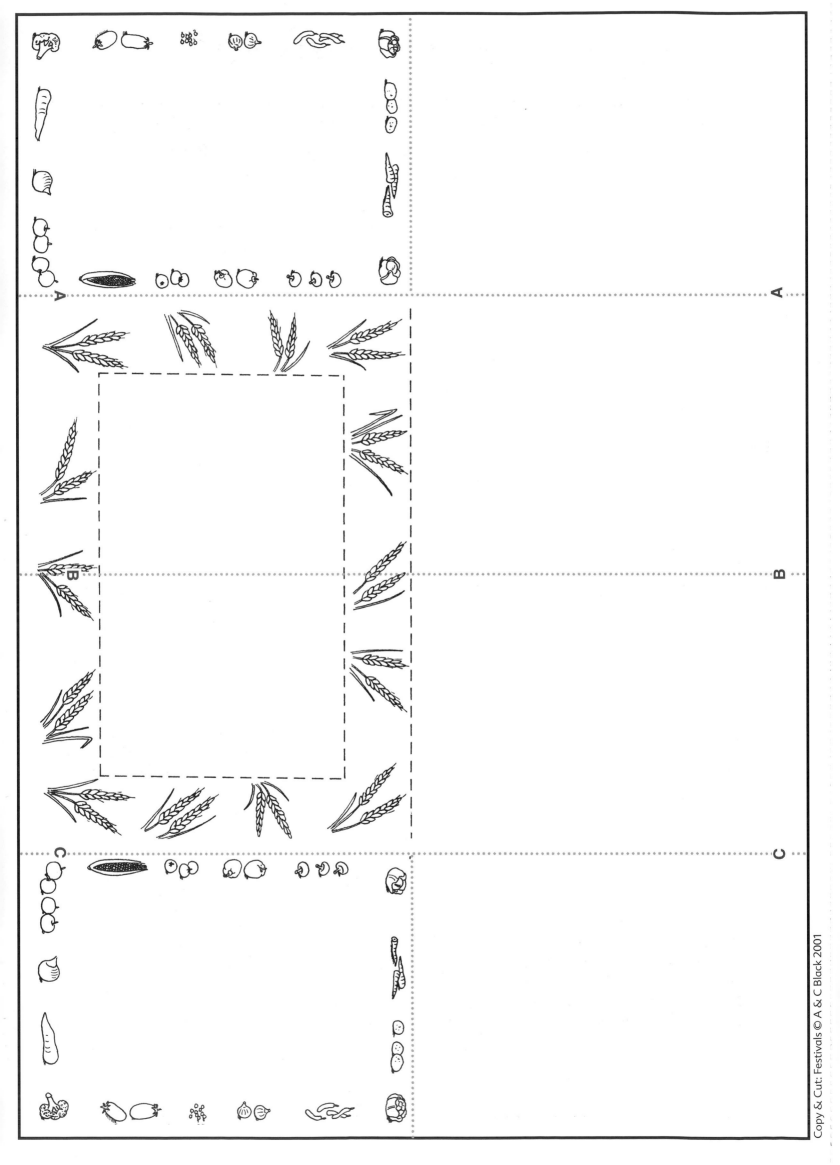

Pesach storybook

Pesach is the most important Jewish festival. It celebrates the time when God helped the Jews to escape from Egypt. Today at Pesach, Jewish people meet up with friends and family and tell the story of the first Pesach. You can tell the story yourself in this storybook.

You will need: the Pesach storybook template • the story of Pesach • scissors • pencil • pencil crayons for decorating

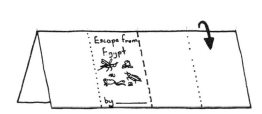

1. Fold the paper in half lengthways, like this.

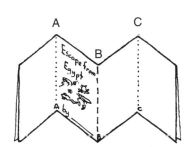

2. Fold the paper in a zig-zag along the dots (A, B, C). Start by folding forwards along the A dots.

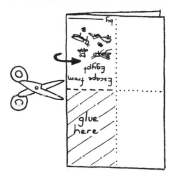

3. Open out the paper fully. Fold in half widthways, like this. Cut along the dashes.

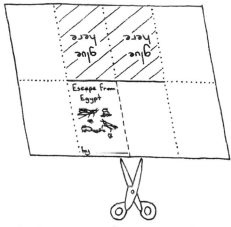

4. Open out the paper. Cut along the dashes from the edge to the centre.

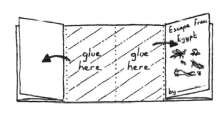

5. Now fold the paper in half lengthways so that the marks are inside. Fold forwards the two middle pages.

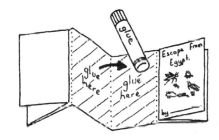

6. Glue together the pages marked 'glue here'. Then fold the covers around the other pages.

Read the story of Pesach. Then plan what you want to put on each page of your book. Write the story on the left-hand pages. Draw pictures to go with the story on the right-hand pages.

Moses asked the king to set the Jews free. The king refused.

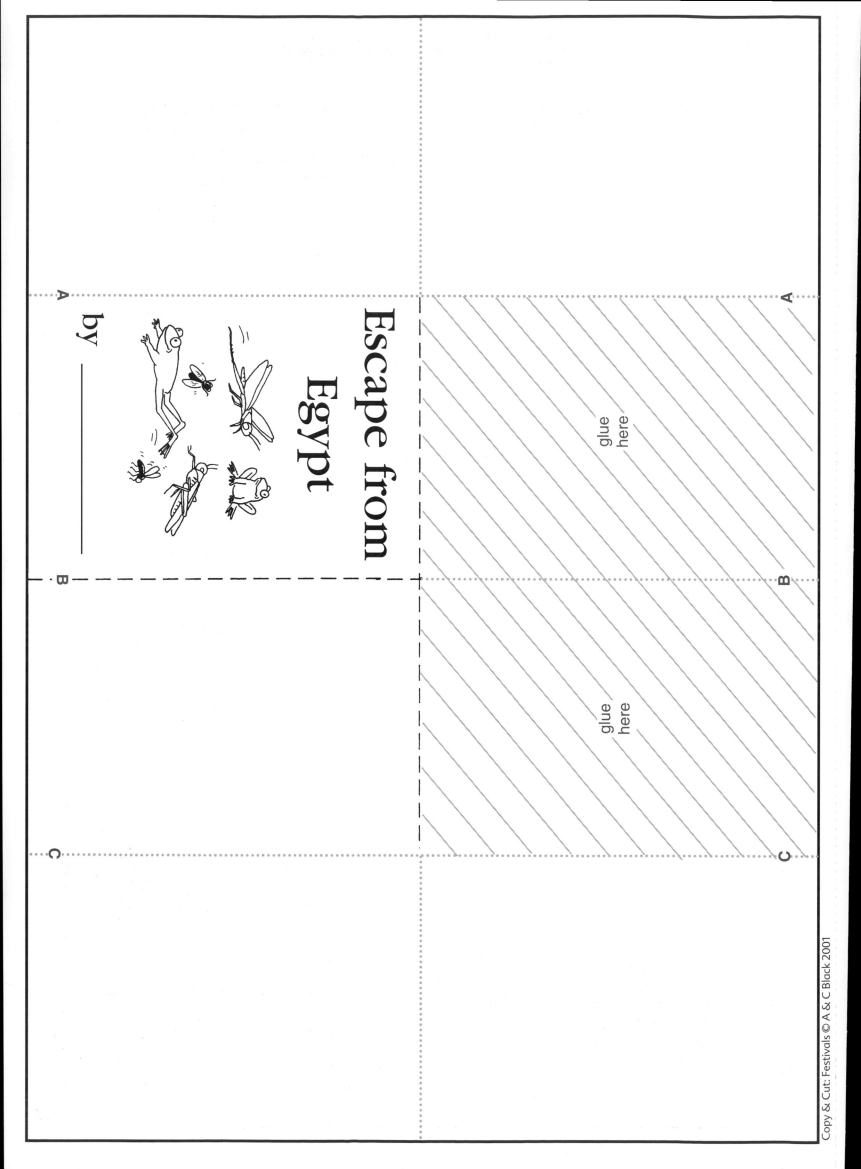

Escape from Egypt

by _____

Seder plate

At Pesach, Jewish people eat a meal called Seder. On the table, there is a Seder plate filled with seven different foods. Each food reminds the people of something that happened to the Jews who lived in Egypt long ago. Draw the foods on your own Seder plate.

You will need: the Seder plate template • scissors • pencil • pencil crayons, magazines or tissue paper and glue for decorating

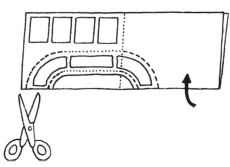

1. Fold the paper in half lengthways, like this. Cut along all the dashes.

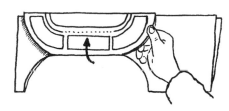

2. Fold the plate shape forwards along the A dots. Then fold backwards. Unfold.

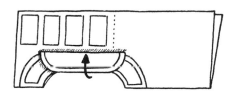

3. Fold forwards along the B dots. Then fold backwards. Unfold.

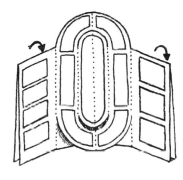

4. Open out the paper. Fold along the C dots, like this.

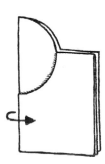

5. Fold the paper in half again.

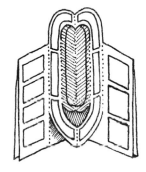

6. Stand up the card. Now pull the plate shape forwards. Push the middle of the plate inwards.

Press the card flat again. On each part of the plate, draw a different food that reminds Jewish people of the first Pesach. You could make a collage of the food using tissue paper or pictures from magazines. Around the sides of the plate, write what the foods are. Find out what they mean.

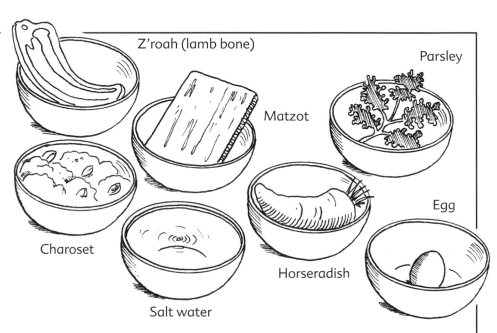

Z'roah (lamb bone)

Parsley

Matzot

Charoset

Horseradish

Egg

Salt water

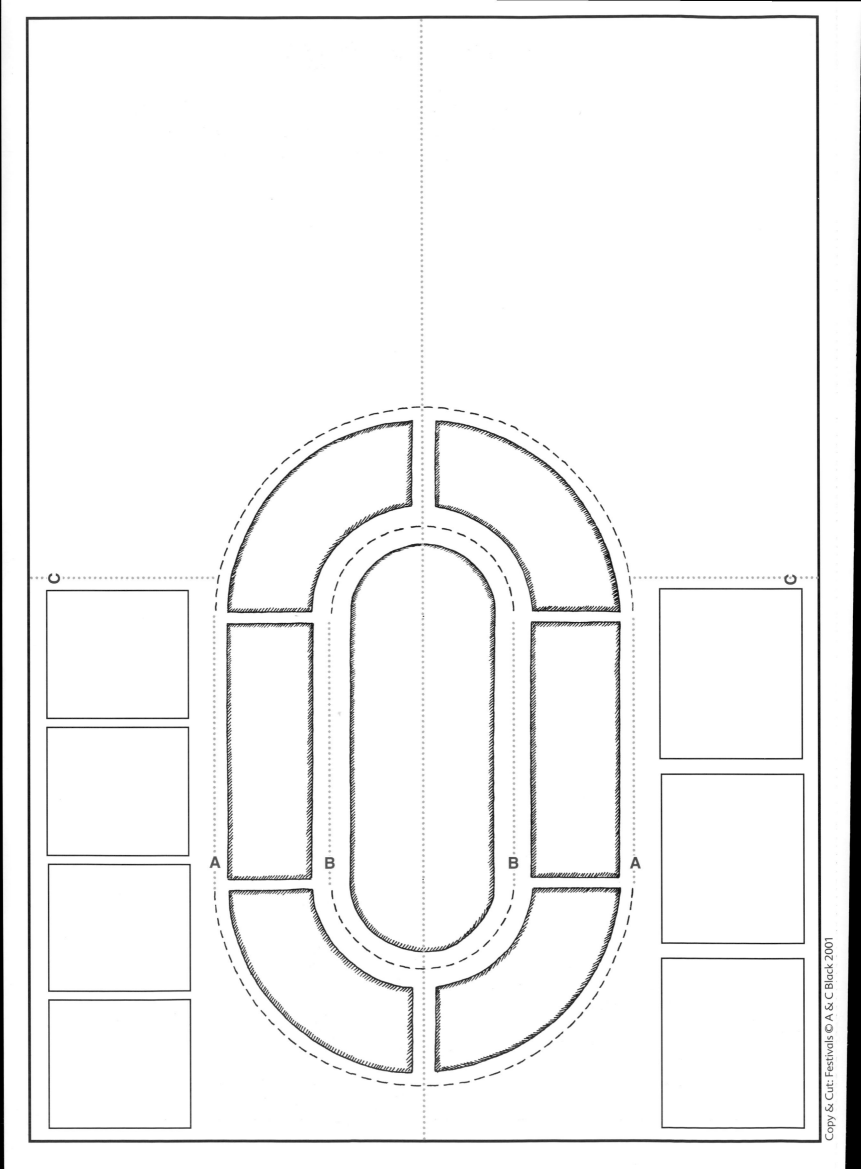

Sukkot hut

Many years ago, the Jews had to travel a long way across the desert. They lived in huts made from branches and leaves. Today, Jewish people celebrate Sukkot to remind them of what happened. Some Jews build huts in their gardens.

You will need: the Sukkot hut template • scissors • glue • pencil • pencil crayons, small twigs, leaves, sand, straw, tissue paper and glitter for decorating

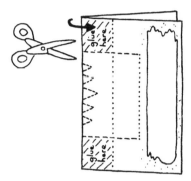

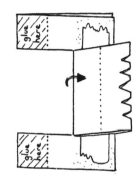

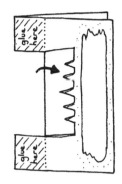

1. Fold the paper in half widthways, like this. Cut along all the dashes.

2. Fold the middle flap forwards. Then fold it backwards. Unfold.

3. Fold forwards along the A dots. Then fold backwards. Unfold.

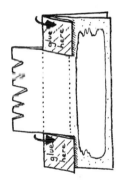

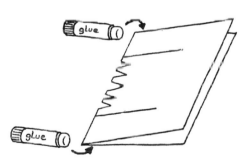

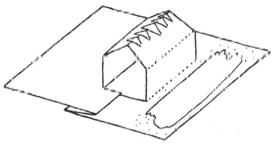

4. Fold forwards along the B dots. Then fold backwards. Unfold.

5. Open out the paper. Carefully glue where marked. Fold the paper in half widthways, with the glue on the inside.

6. Open up the paper. Gently pull up the hut in the middle.

On the base of your model, write about Sukkot. Decorate the hut by gluing on small twigs, leaves, straw and tissue paper. Glue sand to the base. Remember to leave gaps in the roof so that people inside can see the stars at night.

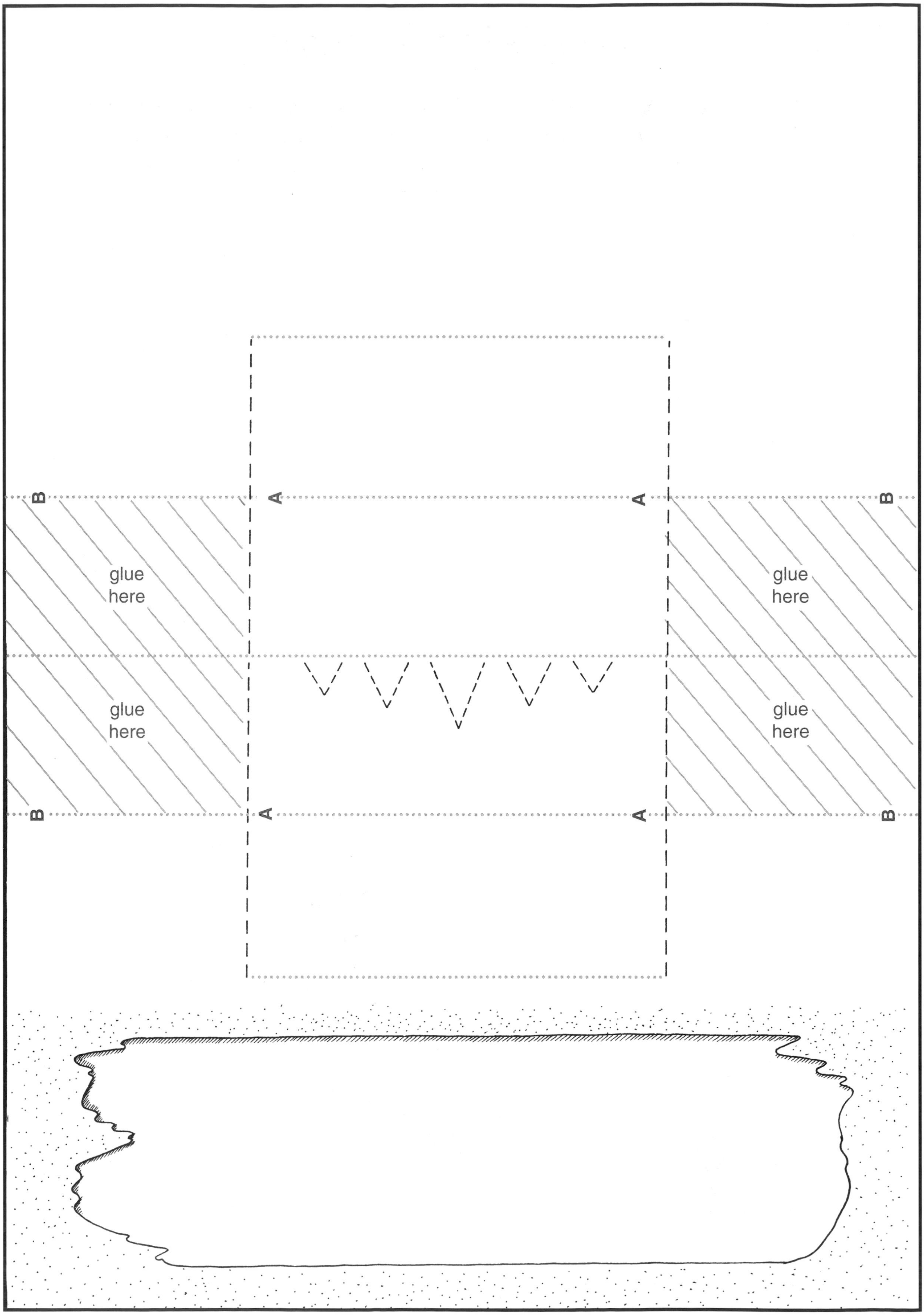

glue
here

glue
here

glue
here

glue
here

A

A

A

A

B

B

B

B

Hanukkah card

Jewish people celebrate the festival of Hanukkah with a candlestick called a hanukiah. It has nine candles, one for each day of the festival and one for lighting all the others. At Hanukkah, Jewish people play games and give each other presents and cards.

You will need: the Hanukkah card template • scissors • pencil • red, orange or yellow tissue paper, gold pen or silver foil and glue for decorating

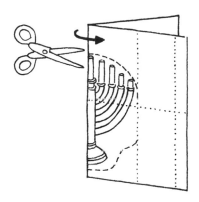

1. Fold the paper in half widthways, like this. Cut along the dashes. Unfold.

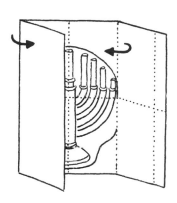

2. Fold the paper forwards along all the A dots. Unfold.

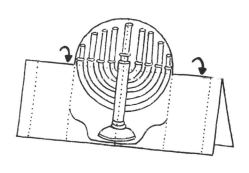

3. Fold the paper backwards along the B dots, like this.

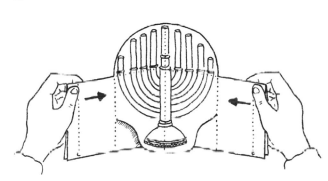

4. Push the left and right edges towards each other. Pull the hanukiah forwards.

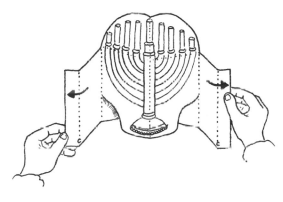

5. Fold outwards along the C dots, like this.

Press the card flat again. Write 'Happy Hanukkah' and a message. On the hanukiah, draw a star and write 'Shalom', which means peace. Decorate the card using a gold pen, or cut shapes from foil and glue them on. Cut flame shapes from tissue paper. Glue them on the candles.

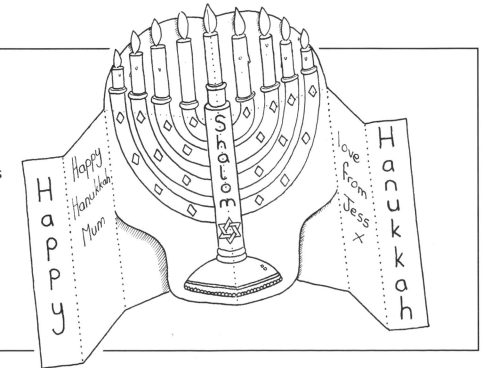

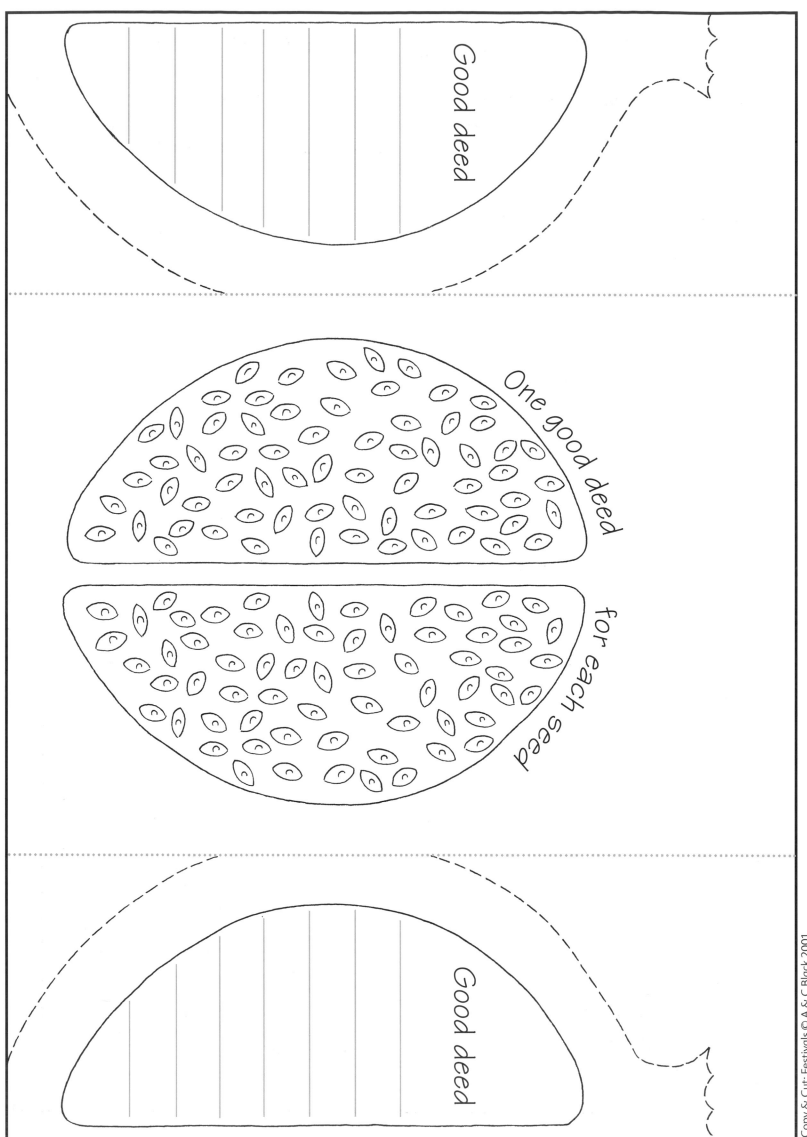

Good deed

One good deed

for each seed

Good deed

Divali finger puppets

Divali is a festival for Hindus and Sikhs. Some Hindus tell the story of Prince Rama and his wife Sita. An evil demon called Ravana kidnapped Sita. Rama and his friend Hanuman set out to rescue her. You can tell the story yourself with these finger puppets.

You will need: the Divali finger puppets template • the story of Rama and Sita • scissors • 6 paper clips • pencil • pencil crayons, glitter or foil, wool and glue for decorating

 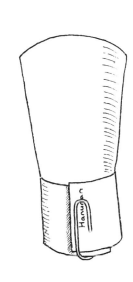 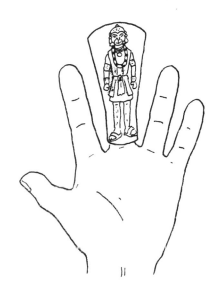

1. Decorate the finger puppets. Cut along the dashes.

2. Ask a friend to help you wrap a puppet around your finger. Use a paper clip to fasten the puppet together.

3. Then turn the puppet round to face you.

Decorate the puppets with bright colours and glitter or foil. You could glue wool on to Hanuman, the monkey general. Then read the story of Rama and Sita. Plan a play using your puppets. You could write a playscript like the one started here.

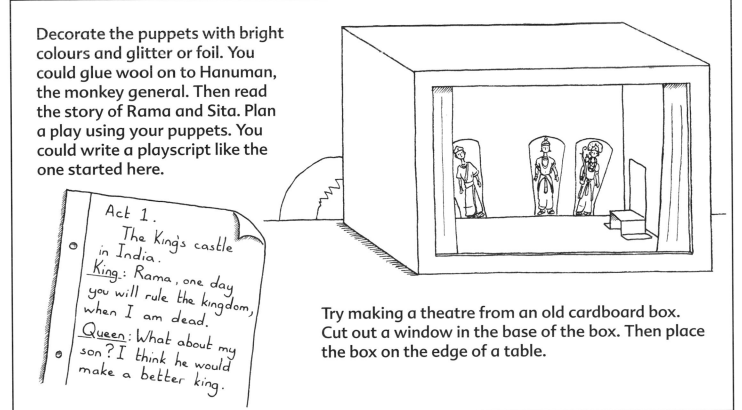

Act 1.
    The King's castle in India.
King: Rama, one day you will rule the kingdom, when I am dead.
Queen: What about my son? I think he would make a better king.

Try making a theatre from an old cardboard box. Cut out a window in the base of the box. Then place the box on the edge of a table.

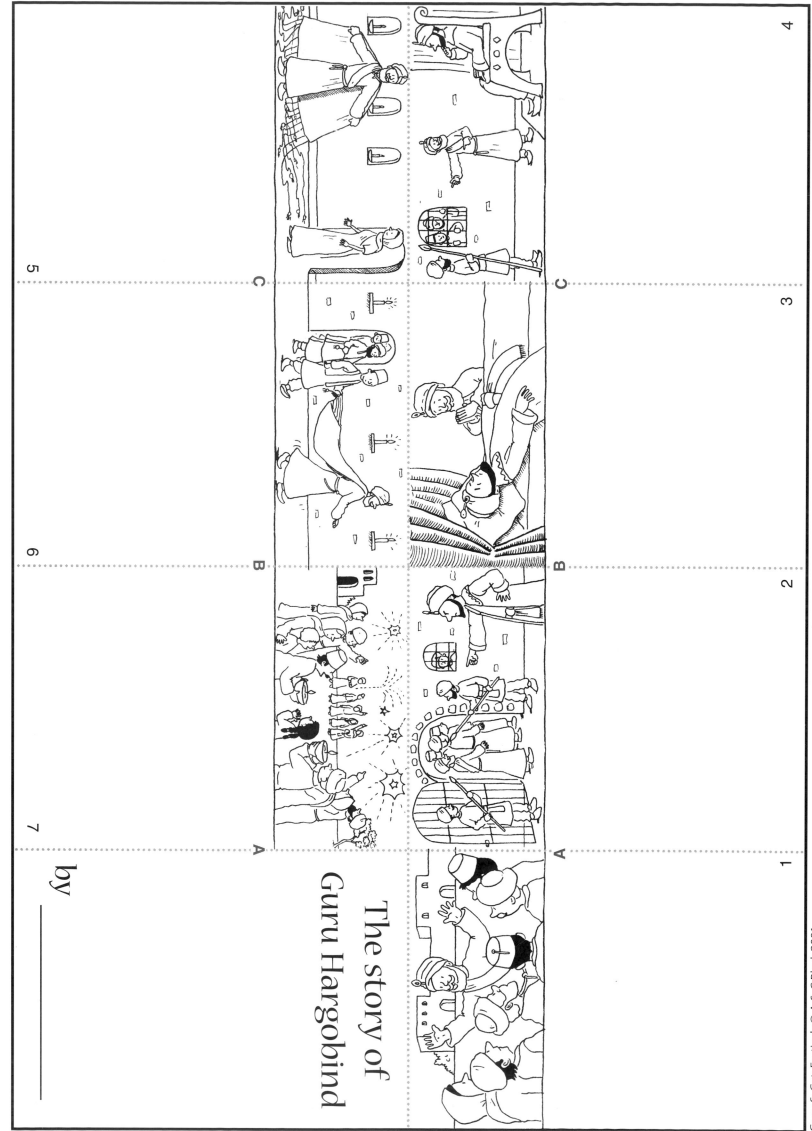

The story of
Guru Hargobind

by _____

Eid sweet box

Eid is a time for giving presents to relatives and friends. Many people give boxes of delicious sweets, made from nuts, dates and honey. They hope that life will be as sweet as the food! Put some tasty Eid treats in your own sweet box and give it to a friend.

You will need: the Eid sweet box template • pencil crayons for decorating

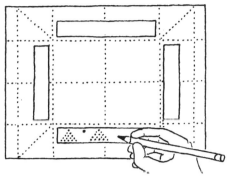

1. Start by drawing Islamic patterns in the boxes.

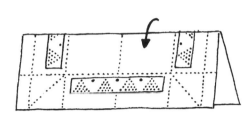

2. Fold the paper in half lengthways, like this. Unfold.

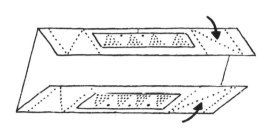

3. Fold the paper backwards along all the A dots, like this. Unfold.

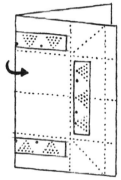

4. Open out the paper. Fold in half widthways, like this. Unfold.

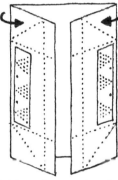

5. Fold backwards along all the B dots, like this. Keep the paper folded.

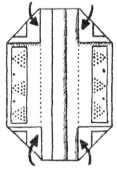

6. Now fold the corners forwards along the C dots.

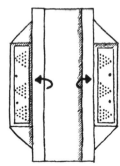

7. Fold outwards along the D dots.

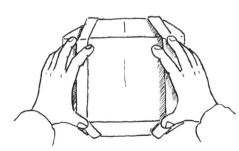

8. Pull up the middle edges to make a box.

Copy one of these Islamic patterns to decorate your box, or design one of your own.

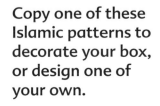

45

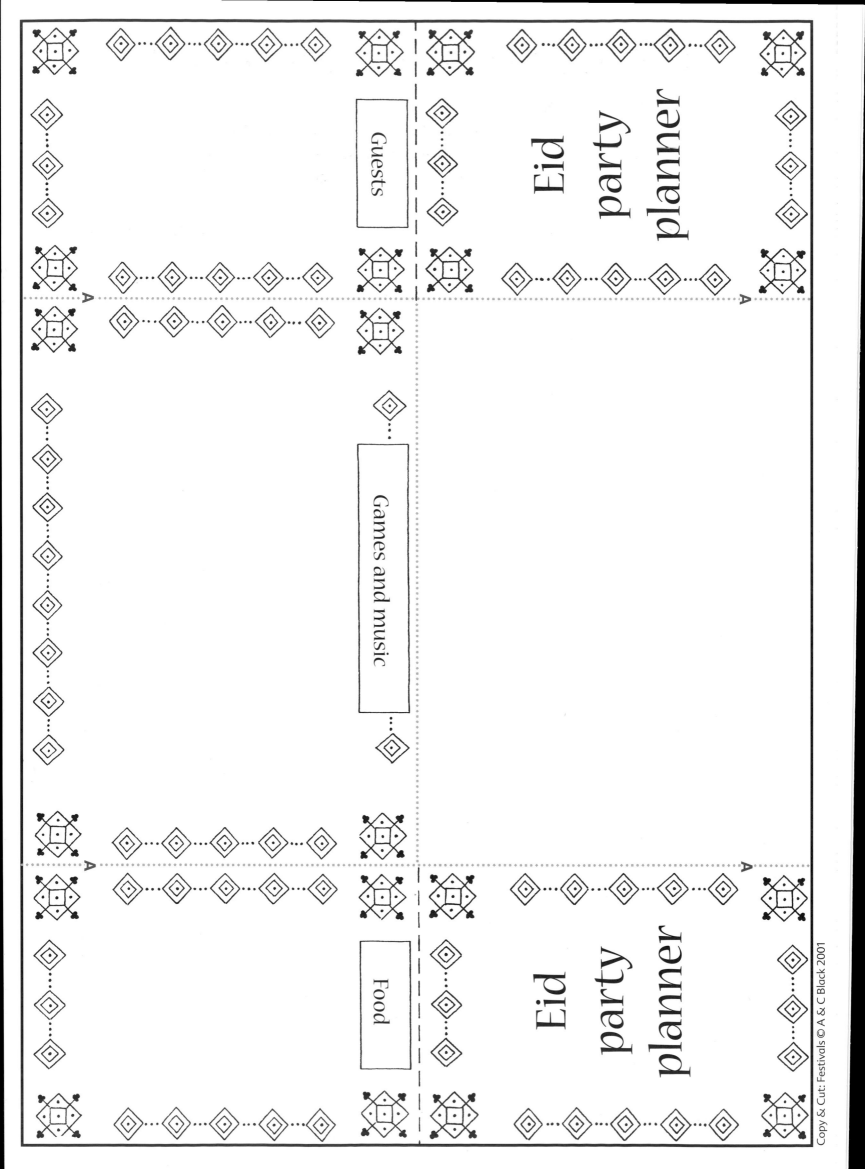

Eid party planner

Guests

Games and music

Eid party planner

Food

Eid party planner

Chinese dragon card

All over the world, Chinese people welcome in the New Year with lively parades. People dress up in colourful dragon costumes and dance along the streets. Musicians bang drums and gongs. The dragon is a friendly creature which brings long life and good luck.

You will need: the Chinese dragon card template • scissors • pencil • sticky paper shapes, red paper and glue for decorating

1. Fold the paper in half lengthways, like this.

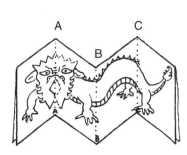

2. Fold the paper in a zig-zag along the dots (A, B, C). Start by folding forwards along the A dots.

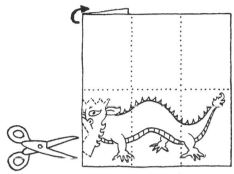

3. Open out the paper fully. Fold along the A dots, like this. Cut along all the dashes.

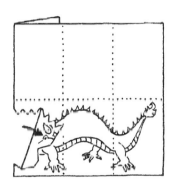

4. Fold forwards along the D dots. Then fold backwards. Unfold.

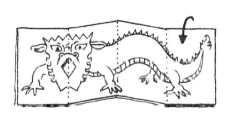

5. Open out the paper. Fold in half lengthways.

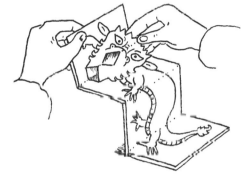

6. Now fold the paper into a zig-zag again. Carefully pull forwards the pop-up head.

Press the card flat again. On the front of your card, you could copy this Chinese message. It says 'Happy New Year!'

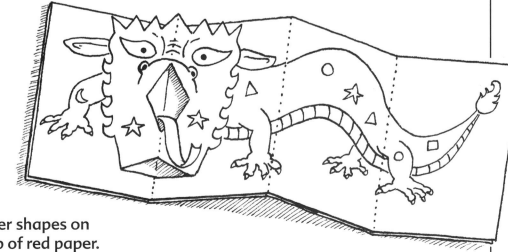

Stick brightly coloured paper shapes on the dragon. Then cut a strip of red paper. Glue one end inside the dragon's mouth to make a tongue.

The story of Pesach

Long ago, the Jewish people lived in Egypt as slaves. They worked hard and they were unhappy. God chose a man called Moses to be their leader. Moses asked the king to set the Jews free. The king refused.

Then God sent ten horrible plagues to Egypt. First, the rivers turned to blood, frogs appeared everywhere, and then lice, and then flies. Next, all the farm animals died and people were covered in painful boils. Then came hailstones, locusts and darkness. Finally, the eldest boy in every Egyptian family died, even the king's son.

The king let the Jews go, but he sent his army to capture them again. When the Jews reached the Red Sea, there seemed to be no escape. But God helped Moses to part the water. The Jews could walk across! The Egyptians followed them, but the water rushed back and they were all drowned.

The Jews lived in the desert for many years. At last, they arrived at a country called Canaan, or Israel. This was the land that God had promised to them.

The story of Holi

There was once an evil king. He thought he was greater than the gods and wanted everyone to worship him. But the king's son, Prahlad, refused. He worshipped the great god, Lord Vishnu. The king was furious and decided to punish Prahlad.

First, the king threw Prahlad from a cliff. But Lord Vishnu saved him just in time, and he floated to the ground. Then the king sent elephants to trample Prahlad. The elephants started to charge, but suddenly they stopped and bowed down in front of him. Lord Vishnu had saved Prahlad again.

Finally, the king's sister said that she would help to kill Prahlad. Her name was Holika and she was a wicked witch.

She built a great bonfire and tried to burn Prahlad in it. But Lord Vishnu was watching. He snatched Prahlad from the flames and wicked Holika died instead.

56

Rama and Sita

King Dasaratha ruled a kingdom in India. His eldest son, Rama, was to be the next king. But Rama's step-mother also had a son. She wanted him to be king instead. So Rama was sent away to live in the forest with his wife, Sita, and his brother, Lakshman.

One day, Rama and Lakshman went out hunting. They wanted to catch a golden deer. While they were gone, an old man came to the door. He was really a ten-headed demon king in disguise. He was called Ravana. Ravana kidnapped Sita and took her to his palace.

Rama searched for Sita but he could not find her. Then a bird told him where Sita was. Rama met up with his friend, Hanuman, the monkey general. They set off with an army to rescue Sita.

Rama fought Ravana and his demon army. A terrible battle raged. Finally, Rama killed Ravana with a golden arrow. Rama and Sita were able to return home to be crowned king and queen. The road was lit with candles to celebrate their return.

The Guru and his cloak

Many years ago, a great Sikh leader called Guru Hargobind lived in India. He was very popular with all the people. But the Emperor was jealous and sent the Guru to prison, along with 52 Hindu princes. The Guru was treated well. But the princes were dressed in rags and they were always hungry.

When the Emperor fell ill, he asked the Guru to pray for him. The Emperor recovered and decided to set the Guru free. Guru Hargobind said that he would only go free if the princes could leave with him. The Emperor replied that only the princes who could hold on to the Guru's cloak could go free. Also, they must leave through a narrow gateway that was only wide enough for one man to pass through.

The clever Guru had a special cloak made. It had 52 silk tassels, which were all different lengths. Each prince held on to a tassel and they all walked free. Everyone celebrated by lighting candles and setting off fireworks.

Epiphany book (pages 13–14)

Give the children copies of the story of the three wise men on page 55 for them to read and plan what they want to draw in their books. Parts of the story are provided on the template as a guide. These could be masked to provide more of a challenge.

 **Easter** commemorates the resurrection of Jesus Christ from the dead. Christians believe this shows that death is not something to fear, but the start of a new life with God. Easter is also a celebration of spring and new life in nature. The word Easter probably derives from an ancient goddess of spring, Eostre. The timing of Easter varies each year and usually falls between mid-March and mid-April.

The week before Easter Sunday is Holy Week. It begins with Palm Sunday, when worshippers are given small palm-leaf crosses to remind them of the day Jesus rode into Jerusalem and was greeted by crowds waving palms. On Maundy Thursday, Jesus shared the Last Supper with his disciples. On Good Friday, he was crucified on a cross. This is a solemn day of prayer. Easter Sunday celebrates the day when Jesus rose

Easter storybook (pages 15–16)

Give the children copies of the Easter story on page 55 for them to read and plan what they want to write in their books. Illustrations are provided on the template as a guide. You could mask the text on the main illustration to provide more of a challenge. Explain to the children that the cross is an important symbol for Christians.

Easter chick (pages 17–18)

Discuss with the children why new life is celebrated at Easter. You could explain that eggs are reminders of how Jesus came back to life.

 In the past, harvest-time was a key event in the farming year, and so a festival was held to thank God for a good harvest. Today **harvest festivals** are held on a Sunday in September or October. Christians decorate churches with fruit, vegetables, flowers and bread. They say prayers and sing hymns of thanks. Afterwards, the food is given away to the needy. Some churches hold a harvest supper. Harvest is celebrated all over the world. In Africa, many tribes celebrate with masked dances.

Harvest display (pages 19–20)

The children may choose whether to draw a harvest scene through the window, or a sketch of a particular fruit or vegetable. If possible, allow them to draw 'from life'. They could write a poem to go with the drawing, or they may wish to write an acrostic of HARVEST, thinking of a different food for each letter. The template for this project could be photocopied on to A3 paper and the finished results used as a wall display.

Jewish festivals

The week-long Jewish festival of **Pesach** (also called Passover) is celebrated in March or April. Jewish people remember the exodus of their descendants from Egypt, where they lived in slavery. The highlight of Pesach is the Seder meal, during which the family retells the story of the first Pesach.

 On the Seder plate there are seven different foods, each of which has a special meaning. A lamb bone is a reminder of the lambs sacrificed in Egypt; a roasted egg is also a reminder of sacrifice; a green herb or vegetable signifies spring; bitter horseradish is a reminder of the Jews' unhappiness; charoset, a sweet paste, represents the mortar used by the Jews in their work in Egypt; salt water stands for the tears shed during slavery; and flat, dry crackers, called matzot, remind Jews of the unleavened bread their ancestors baked just before they escaped (they were unable to wait for the dough to rise).

Pesach storybook (pages 21–22)

Give the children copies of the story of Pesach on page 56 for them to read and plan what they want to write and draw in their books.

Seder plate (pages 23–24)

This project works particularly well when enlarged to A3 size. Before the children begin to draw and label their models, discuss with them the different foods that are put on the plate (see above).

The festival of **Sukkot** takes place in September or October. Jews remember how their ancestors lived in temporary homes and were looked after by God, following their exodus from Egypt. The festival's name comes from the name of the huts, sukkot (singular sukkah). Some Jews build sukkot in their gardens and eat their meals there during the seven days of the festival. Another Sukkot custom is the taking of the four plants at a service in the synagogue. People walk around the synagogue, holding three branches — palm, myrtle and willow — in one hand, and a citron branch in the other. The plants are reminders of harvest-time. Each plant also stands for a part of the body, to remind people to worship God with their whole being.

Sukkot hut (pages 25—26)

Explain to the children that Jews leave gaps in the roof so that the stars remind them of God's care and guidance.

 **Hanukkah** (meaning dedication) is the Jewish festival of lights in December. It commemorates the struggle between the Jews and Antiochus, King of Syria, in the second century BCE. The king marched on Jerusalem and ransacked the Temple, the Jews' holiest place. A group of Jews, called the Maccabees, led a rebellion. When they relit the everlasting Temple lamp, they found only enough oil to last for one day. By a miracle, God kept the lamp burning for eight days until more oil arrived. Jews celebrate by lighting a hanukiah, an eight-branched candlestick. They sing songs, exchange gifts, play games and eat food such as latkes (potato cakes) and sufganiyot (doughnuts).

Hanukkah card (pages 27—28)

The children could stick the flames on the candles day by day, to represent the lighting of a candle on each day of the festival.

 Rosh Hashanah is the Jewish New Year. It falls in September or October and celebrates the creation of the world, the day of judgement and the renewal of the bond between God and the Jews. It is the start of ten 'Days of Returning', when people think about the wrongs they have done and promise to do better. Over the two days of Rosh Hashanah, there are services in the synagogue and the shofar is blown. This is a musical instrument made from a ram's horn, which makes a sound like a trumpet. Blowing the shofar has many meanings, including a call for healing and strength.

Rosh Hashanah card (pages 29—30)

You may wish to provide suggestions of good deeds that the children could write on their cards.

Hindu festivals

 **Holi** falls in February or March. It is a joyful spring festival celebrating the triumph of good over evil. This is illustrated by the story of Prahlad and Holika, who gave the festival its name. Hindus also remember episodes from the childhood of Lord Krishna, one of the most popular Hindu gods. Krishna is famous for his love of mischief and for playing tricks on his friends. On the night before Holi, bonfires are built to remind people of Holika's story. The following day, people have fun playing tricks and drenching each other with coloured water, to remember the games Krishna played. The festival lasts for two or three days.

Holi elephant book (pages 31—32)

Give the children copies of the story of Holi on page 56, for them to read and plan what they want to write in their books. The first two pages of the book have been completed to get the children started; these can be masked before photocopying to make the activity more challenging.

 **Divali,** or Deepavali (both names mean a garland of lights) is in October or November. There are various reasons for celebrating Divali. For some Hindus, Divali marks the start of the New Year. Many people also remember the story of Rama and Sita, and celebrate their return from exile. For others, particularly business people, the most important part of Divali is Lakshmi Puja, when they pray to the goddess Lakshmi for good fortune in the year to come. For all Hindus, the most important message of Divali is the triumph of good over evil, and of hope and happiness for the future.

In Britain, Hindus celebrate on the weekend nearest to the actual days of Divali. Hindu mandirs (temples) organise firework displays and sumptuous dinners. In India, the celebrations usually last for five days. Each day has its own customs and rituals. On the first evening, a single diva (lamp) is lit and offered to Yama, Lord of Death. The following day, Hindus rise early, bathe, put on clean clothes and enjoy a special breakfast, to celebrate the victory of Lord Krishna over an evil demon. Day three is Lakshmi Puja, when Hindus worship Lakshmi, the goddess of wealth and good fortune. Divas are lit to welcome the goddess into people's homes. The fourth day is a day for starting new ventures. Children are given new clothes and many Hindus go to the mandir, visit friends and relations, and exchange gifts of food, especially Indian sweets. Day five is Sisters' Day, when brothers visit their sisters' houses for delicious meals.

Divali finger puppets (pages 33–34)

Give the children copies of the story of Rama and Sita on page 57 for them to read and plan what they want to include in their plays. Ensure that the children decorate the puppets before cutting them out. Fixing the puppets with sticky tape will make them secure. It may be easier for some children to have them stuck on lolly sticks. A group could decorate a box for a stage and make scenery for the play.

Diva candle (pages 35–36)

To introduce the activity, sit the children in a circle with the lights off. Ask them to think about how they feel while they are sitting in the dark. Then light a candle and ask them to think about how they feel now. Encourage the children to use their thoughts as ideas for what to write on their diva candles. Ensure that the children decorate and write on the candles before they glue them together.

Divali card (pages 37–38)

This project could be adapted to use as a Sikh greeting card.

Divali henna card (pages 39–40)

Show the children photographs of Hindu women with henna patterns on their hands and feet. You could use real henna to copy the patterns on to their hands.

Sikh festivals

Divali is an important festival for Sikhs as well as for Hindus, although it is celebrated for a different reason. For Sikhs, the most important aspect of Divali is remembering Guru Hargobind's release from prison in 1619. He was imprisoned by the Mughal emperor of India, Jahangir. Guru Hargobind's insistence that 52 princes be released with him shows that he was willing to sacrifice his own freedom for others.

At Divali, divas are lit to welcome the Guru home. In Amritsar, Guru Hargobind's hometown, the whole of the Golden Temple is lit up. There are also bonfires and firework displays.

Sikh Divali book (pages 41–42)

Give the children copies of the story of the Guru and his cloak on page 57 for them to read and plan what they want to write in their books.

Muslim festivals

The two most important Islamic festivals are the two Eids, **Eid-ul-Fitr** and Eid-ul-Adha, when Muslims pray, visit friends and relatives, share food and exchange gifts and cards. Eid-ul-Fitr marks the end of Ramadan, the month of fasting. It begins with the new moon and lasts for three days. Before Eid, Muslims give money to the poor, which is one of the Five Pillars, or duties, of Islam. The moon and stars are important symbols in Islam.

In the weeks leading up to Eid, homes are cleaned and decorated, special food is planned, gifts are chosen for friends, new outfits are bought, Eid prayers are said, friends and relatives are visited and people hug each other.

Eid mosque (pages 43–44)

Encourage the children to bring in pictures of mosques, and to look carefully at the way they are decorated.

Eid sweet box (pages 45–46)

Ensure that the children decorate the paper before they make the box. If possible, children could bring in a small sweet selection or sugared almonds to put in their boxes. Alternatively, they could make sweets to go in the boxes, using the recipe below.

Coconut Barfi

Sugar	1 cup
Water	1 cup
Desiccated coconut	1 cup
cardamoms (crushed)	6
Chopped cashew nuts	½ cup
Ghee or butter	2 tsp

1. Heat the sugar and water on a low heat to make a thick syrup.
2. Remove any scum from the syrup. Add the coconut and crushed cardamoms and mix.
3. Remove from the heat while the mixture is a thick pouring consistency.
4. Add the chopped cashews and mix.
5. Pour the mixture onto a plate greased with the ghee. Spread it out quickly with a knife.
6. Cut into diamond-shaped pieces.

Eid party planner (pages 47—48)

Encourage the children to record details for their party, including who to invite, what to wear, games and music to play and a list of Halal foods (meaning clean — containing no pork products or alcohol). They could write ideas for classroom decorations, for example, paper chains, streamers and tinsel draped around doors and windows in the shapes of domes, arches and crescents. The children could learn this song, for inclusion in their planners, and make up a tune for it.

Sing Eid Mubarak
It's time for joy
Sing Eid Mubarak
Every girl and boy
Our clothes are new
We're looking fine
Sing Eid Mubarak
It's a happy time

Chinese festivals

Chinese New Year is celebrated in January or February by Chinese communities all over the world. It is a time for sweeping out the old and looking forward to a fresh start. Traditionally, preparations begin one week earlier, when the family gathers to worship the kitchen god, Tsao-shen, who oversees all members of the household. At New Year, the god returns to heaven to report on each person's conduct during the past year.

The festival officially lasts for three days. Houses are cleaned and decorated with lanterns and lights in the lucky colours of red and gold, which symbolise health, wealth and wisdom. Children receive gifts of money, wrapped in red paper. Colour and symbolism are also important in the food eaten at New Year, for example, noodles are eaten for long life and red foods, such as prawns, are said to bring good luck and happiness. In many communities, the highlights of the festival are the spectacular street parades, featuring the dragon and lion dances.

Chinese dragon card (pages 49—50)

The children could think of good luck messages to go inside the card.

Chinese lantern (pages 51—52)

Ensure that the children decorate the paper before gluing the lantern together, but without obscuring the gluing area. You could display the lanterns by threading the handles on to a piece of string and tying it across the room.

Buddhist festivals

The festival of **Wesak**, also known as Buddha Day, takes place at the time of the full moon in April or May. It is the most important festival in the Buddhist year, commemorating the Buddha's birth, enlightenment and death. The Buddha gained enlightenment while meditating under a tree in Bodh Gaya, India. He realised that the reason for suffering in the world was that people were never content with their lot. The Buddha spent the rest of his life teaching people how to find a way out of suffering, by following the Noble Eightfold Path.

Lotus flower (pages 53—54)

The lotus flower is an important symbol of the Buddha's enlightenment. Children could place the flowers in a basket, or string them up in the classroom as decorations.

Calendar of festivals

	Buddhist	Chinese 福	Christian ✝	Hindu	Jewish	Muslim	Sikh
January		Chinese New Year	Epiphany (6)				
February							
March			Easter	Holi			
April			Easter		Pesach		
May	Wesak						
June							
July							
August							
September			Harvest		Rosh Hashanah		
October			Harvest		Sukkot		
November				Divali			Divali
December			Christmas (25)		Hanukkah	Eid-ul-Fitr	

Note: This calendar shows only the festivals associated with projects in this book. Most festival dates vary from year to year. This may depend on the phases of the moon, or the start of the religious year. Specific dates are provided only where they do not vary.

Useful contacts

You can find out more about the festivals featured in this book, along with extra pictures and patterns for decorating the projects, by visiting the following websites or contacting the organisations below.

Websites

General
www.theresite.org.uk
www.theholidayspot.com
www.holidayfestival.com
www.holidays.net
http://www.re-xs.ucsm.ac.uk
www.frenchwood.co.uk/startpage.htm

Buddhism
www.buddhanet.net

Chinese New Year
www.chinatownonline.co.uk/pages
/new_year
www.chinascape.org/index/culture
/holidays

Christianity
www.christianity.about.com
www.bbc.co.uk/religion/religions
/christianity

Hinduism
www.hindunet.org/festivals
www.indiancultureonline.com/festival
/i_hindu.htm

Islam
www.ifgstl.org/html/basics/basicsnf.
htm
http://cnug.clackesd.k12.or.us/wood/A
M%20ISLAM/islam.htm

Judaism
www.joi.org/celebrate
www.jewfaq.org

Sikhism
www.sikhmuseum.org.

Addresses

Board of Deputies of British Jews
Commonwealth House
1–19 New Oxford Street
London WC1A 1NU
Tel: 020 7543 5400

The Buddhist Society
58 Eccleston Square
London SW1V 1PH
Tel: 020 7834 5858

Christian Education Movement
Royal Buildings
Victoria Street
Derby DE1 1GW
Tel: 01332 296655

The Hindu Centre
39 Grafton Terrace
London NW5 4JA
Tel: 020 7485 8200

Muslim Information Centre
233 Seven Sisters Road
London N4 2DA
Tel: 020 7272 5170

Sikh Missionary Society
10 Featherstone Road
Southall
Middlesex UB2 5AA
Tel: 020 8574 1902